The Amazing Music Funbook

Games & Puzzles

NOTES   RESTS

Published by
Wise Publications
14-15 Berners Street,
London W1T 3LJ, UK.

Exclusive Distributors:
Music Sales Limited
Distribution Centre, Newmarket Road,
Bury St Edmunds, Suffolk IP33 3YB, UK.
Music Sales Pty Limited
20 Resolution Drive, Caringbah,
NSW 2229, Australia.

Order No. AM995269
ISBN 978-1-84772-716-9

Edited by Rachel Payne.
Design and Layout by Camden Music.
Puzzles devised by Christopher Hussey.

Your Guarantee of Quality
As publishers, we strive to produce every book to the
highest commercial standards.
Particular care has been given to specifying acid-free, neutral-sized paper
made from pulps which have not been elemental chlorine bleached.
This pulp is from farmed sustainable forests and was
produced with special regard for the environment.
Throughout, the printing and binding have been planned to
ensure a sturdy, attractive publication which should give years of enjoyment.
If your copy fails to meet our high standards,
please inform us and we will gladly replace it.

www.musicsales.com

Wise Publications
part of The Music Sales Group
London/New York/Paris/Sydney/Copenhagen/Berlin/Madrid/Tokyo

Amy the archer

Amy needs help working out which arrow she should aim at which target! She needs to match the note durations with their rests.

Draw a line from the tip of each arrow to the target they should aim for.

Handy Hint

♪ = quaver = ½ beat 𝄾
♩ = crotchet = 1 beat 𝄽
𝅗𝅥 = minim = 2 beats 𝄼
𝅝 = semibreve = 4 beats 𝄻

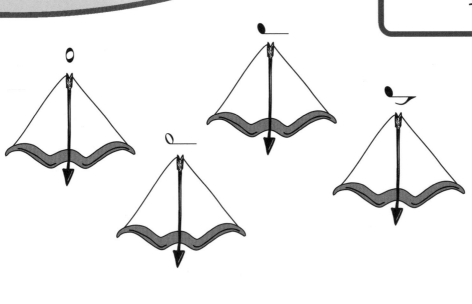

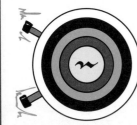

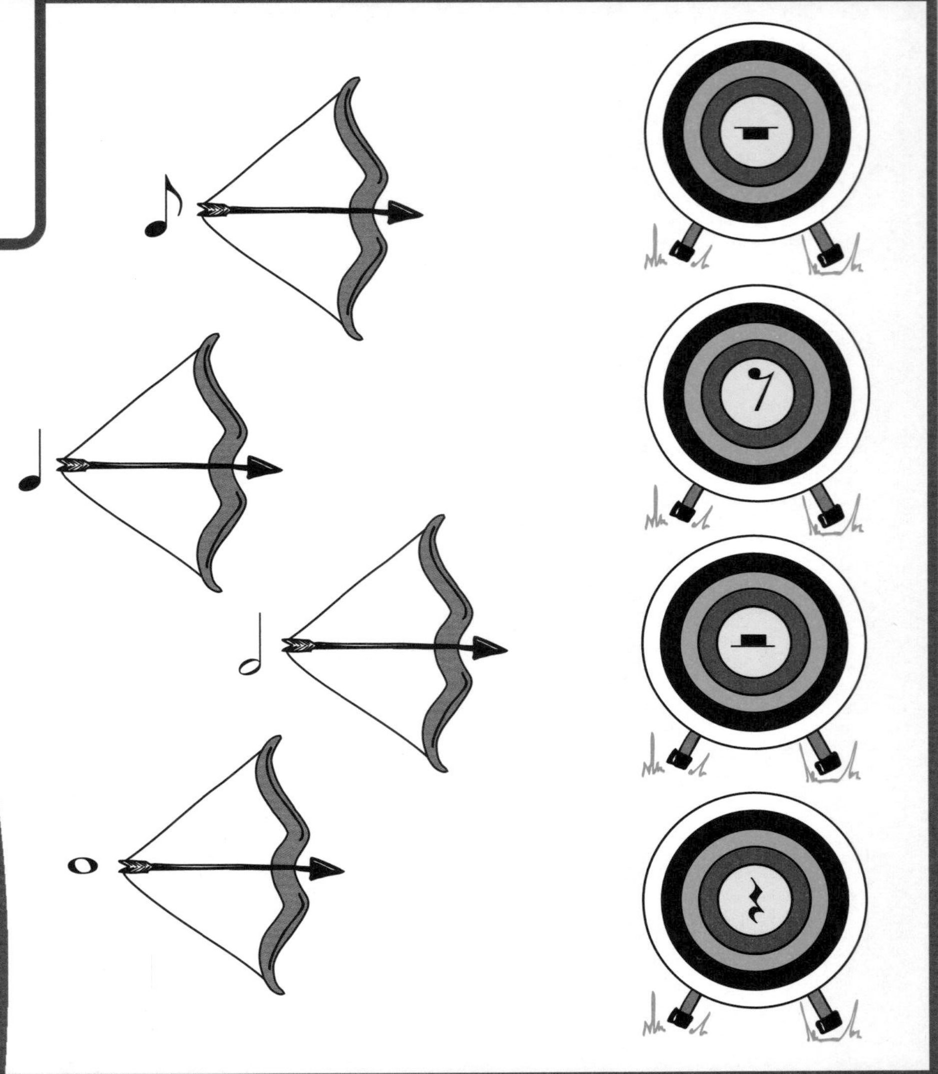

Chloë's clefs

Chloë needs some help counting how many treble clefs are hiding in this pile of musical symbols.

How many are there?

How many bass clefs are there?

Handy Hint

A treble clef looks like this: 𝄞

A bass clef looks like this: 𝄢

Eleanor has spilt her milkshake over the words below. Can you help her work out what the missing letter in each word should be?

Handy Hint
They are all percussion instruments.

tr_angle

x_lophone

cla_es

sn_re d_um

cym_al

t_mbourine

Be more careful with your milkshake next time Eleanor!

Rosy's rock rhythms

There are seven differences between Rosy's drum kit and Imogen's. Can you spot them and circle them on Rosy's drum kit?

Imogen's drum kit

Imogen

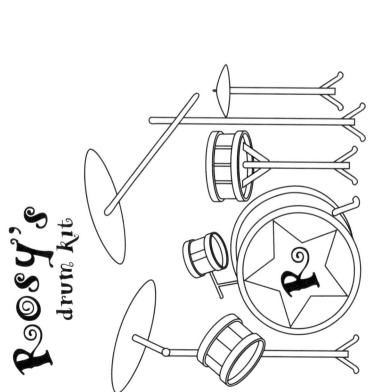

Rosy's drum kit

Now colour in both drum kits.

Molly's amazing maze

Molly has got her violin bow, but that's no use on its own! She'll need to find a way to the centre of the maze to find her violin. Can you help her?

Can you see any musical notes hiding in the hedges?

Lizzie's loopy lines

Lizzie has drawn a loopy line between the **reed** and the instrument it is used to play—the **clarinet**. Can you draw your own loopy lines in different colours to join the things that make the sound to their correct instrument?

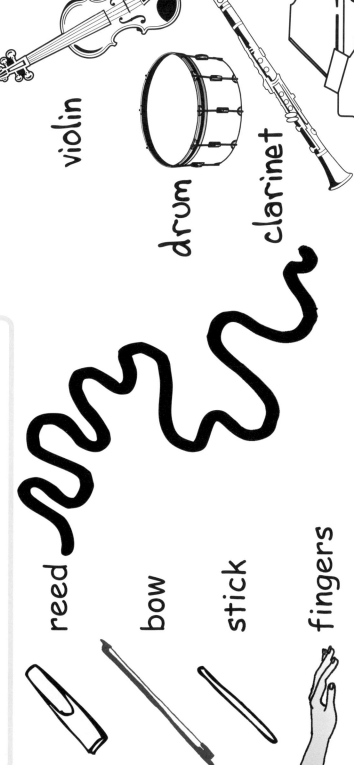

violin

drum

clarinet

piano

reed

bow

stick

fingers

Now colour the instruments.

Handy Hint

Reeds are for woodwind instruments
Bows are for string instruments
Sticks are for percussion instruments
Fingers are for keyboard instruments

Harry's happy families

trumpet

bass drum

violin

clarinet

trombone

cello

triangle

flute

Harry is trying to work out which family each of the orchestral instruments comes from. Can you draw a wiggly arrow to where each of them live? (The first has been drawn for you!)

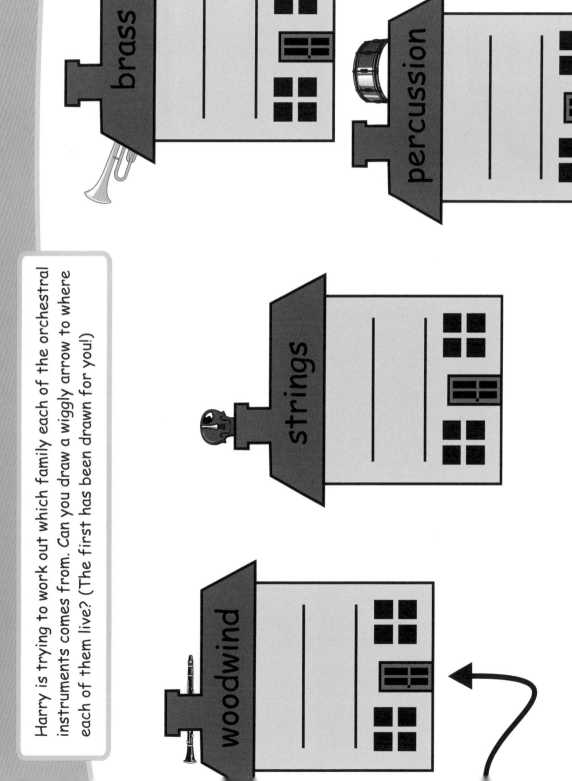

Now copy the names of the instruments into the houses they belong to.

Ann's animals

How loud or soft is the sound that each of Ann's animals makes? Match each animal with the correct symbol and word by drawing lines between them.

very soft

loud

$f\!f$

p

very loud

f

soft

$p\!p$

Handy Hint

pp = pianissimo = very soft
p = piano = soft
f = forte = loud
$f\!f$ = fortissimo = very loud

Now colour all the animals.

Are you sure all these animals are your pets Ann?!

Can you help Sophie balance her seesaw by adding the number of beats together and then writing the answer on the seesaw? Sophie has done the first one for you.

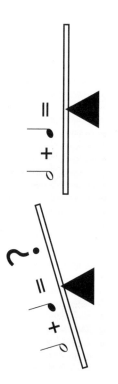

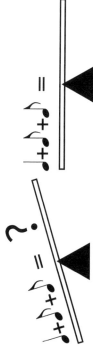

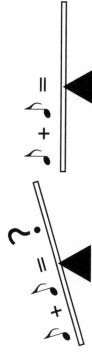

Handy Hint

♪ = quaver = ½
♩ = crotchet = 1
𝅗𝅥 = minim = 2

Stephanie's steps

Stephanie loves music and she sings all around the house, even when she's going up the stairs! Can you help Stephanie work out the difference between instruments that make high sounds and instruments that make low sounds by writing the name of each instrument below on the correct step? Put the highest instrument on the top step and the lowest on the bottom step.

recorder

piccolo

cello

tuba

low

William's wordsearch

Can you help William by finding the six members of the woodwind family that are hidden in this wordsearch? Circle the words when you find them.

A	C	R	O	B	O	C	M	N
O	L	O	C	C	I	P	O	R
S	A	X	O	P	H	O	N	E
H	R	A	L	C	S	B	I	T
T	I	S	E	S	P	A	H	U
A	N	J	A	O	A	S	X	L
L	E	B	L	L	B	S	O	F
F	T	E	C	I	P	O	X	R

PICCOLO

FLUTE

OBOE

BASSOON

CLARINET

SAXOPHONE

Handy Hint

The words can go up, down, across or diagonally in any direction!

Which instrument is this?

_ _ _ _ _ _ _ _ _ _ _

Oliver's odd-one-out

Oliver has accidentally put one wrong instrument, which doesn't match the others, in each box. Can you spot the odd-one-out in each box and circle them?

Can you write the names of the odd-ones-out in their correct boxes? Now colour each box a different colour to help Oliver next time!

Handy Hint
Look at the label on the top of each box to help you!

WOODWIND
clarinet
bassoon
tuba
oboe

STRINGS
violin
cello
flute
double bass

BRASS
triangle
trombone
trumpet
horn

PERCUSSION
xylophone
viola
woodblock
bass drum

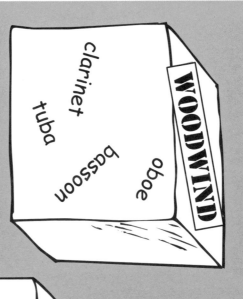

Thomas's tractor

Can you colour Thomas's tractor block-by-block using the musical symbols to tell you which colour to use in each block?

Below is a key to the musical symbol colouring code.

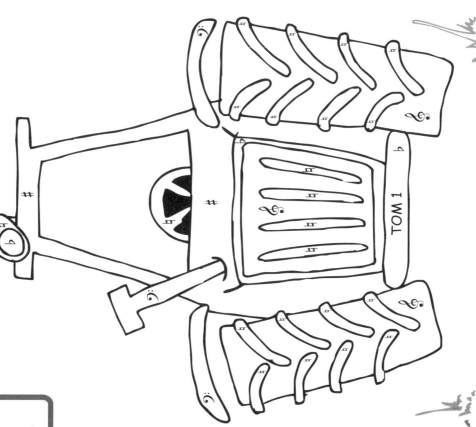

Colour blocks with a...

natural ♮ grey

bass clef 𝄢 blue

flat ♭ yellow

treble clef 𝄞 black

sharp ♯ red

Now draw your face behind the steering wheel.

Bethany's brass

Bethany likes the sound that brass instruments make the best! Find the names of the brass instruments and colour them yellow.

How many are there? ☐

Can you spot any instruments with strings? How many? ☐

drum

recorder

trumpet

cello

violin

xylophone

clarinet

tuba

banjo

piano

horn

harp

Tyler's train

Tyler's train has one carriage for notes and one carriage for their rests. Can you help him by drawing the notes and rests below in the right places?

Put the notes in one carriage in order of length, starting with the shortest, and their rests in the same order in the other. Tyler has already drawn in the shortest note (a quaver) and its rest.

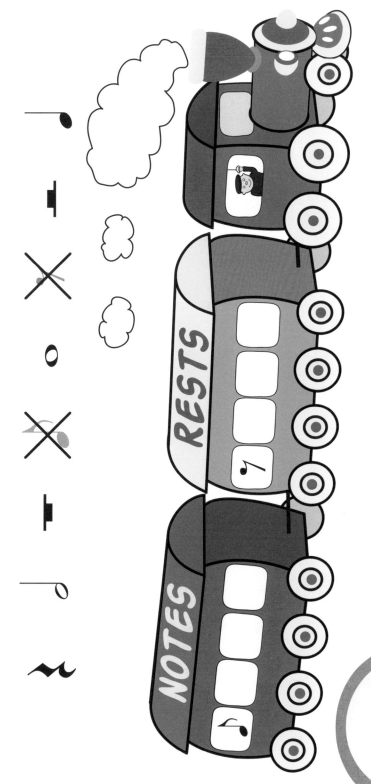

Handy Hint

Have a look at Amy the archer on page 2.

Draw a short note here:

Draw a long note here:

Ella's _ _ _ _ _ _

???

Join the dots and find out what instrument Ella plays!

Start here

Now write in the names of Ella's instrument at the top of the page, on the lines. Can you colour the instrument in? What's missing from Ella's instrument?

Handy Hint

Here are some letters to help you:

E L _ _ T R _ _
G _ _ _ T _ R

Dylan's dinosaurs

Can you match the dinosaurs with the instruments that begin with same letter? Draw a line between each dinosaur and their instrument.

Sarah the Stegosaurus

Terence the Tyrannosaurus Rex

David the Diplodocus

Now colour in the dinosaurs and their musical instruments.

Grace's guessing game

Grace has described five musical instruments below, but she doesn't know what they are called. Can you help her by choosing the correct answer and putting a circle around it?

1   This instrument has 88 keys – some are black and some are white...

banjo   violin   piano   glockenspiel

2   This instrument is played with a bow and has a spike at the bottom...

harpsichord   cello   bongo   ukulele

3   This is a percussion instrument and also the name of a shape...

tambourine   drum   triangle   xylophone

4   This is a large instrument with lots of strings, and it's played without using a bow...

harp   recorder   oboe   gong

5   This instrument has lots of wooden bars that you hit with a mallet or beater...

clarinet   xylophone   drum   harmonica

Megan's Magic Spells

Megan uses tunes in her spells to make useful things. Write down the letter names of the notes below and match each tune with the item it spells.

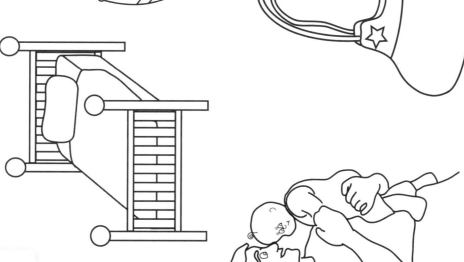

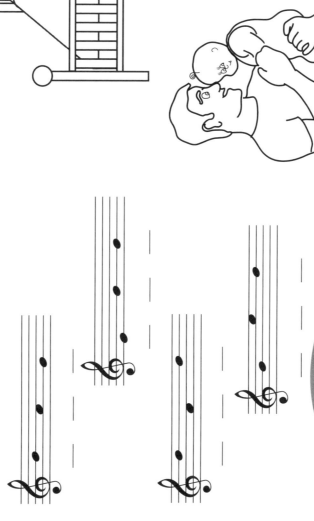

Handy Hint

Here are the names of the notes on the treble clef:

E F G A B C D E

Now colour in the pictures and add your own pretty patterns.

Callum's crossword

Can you solve the clues and fill in the crossword? To help you, Callum has already filled in some of the letters.

Clues

1. I am a woodwind instrument and I have a double reed.

2. I am the biggest and lowest instrument in the brass family.

3. I am a note that lasts for one beat.

4. I have four strings and a spike that rests on the floor.

5. I am the clef used for higher notes.

Puzzle solutions

Amy the archer (page 2)

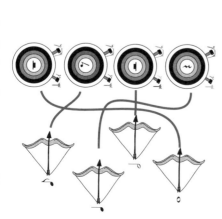

Rosy's rock rhythms (page 5)

Harry's happy families (page 8)

woodwind
flute
clarinet

strings
violin
cello

brass
trumpet
trombone

percussion
triangle
bass drum

Ann's animals (page 10)

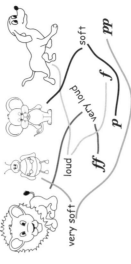

very soft — pp

soft — p

very loud — f

loud — ff

Sophie's seesaws (page 11)

𝅗𝅥 + 𝅘𝅥 = 3   𝅘𝅥𝅮 + 𝅘𝅥. = 1

𝅘𝅥 + 𝅘𝅥𝅮 + 𝅘𝅥. = 4   𝅘𝅥𝅮 + 𝅘𝅥𝅮 + 𝅘𝅥𝅮 = 2

Stephanie's steps (page 12)

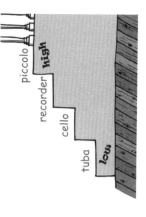

piccolo — **high**

recorder

cello

tuba — **low**

Molly's amazing maze (page 6)

Chloë's clefs (page 3)

How many treble clefs are there? 4

How many bass clefs are there? 4

Lizzy's loopy lines (page 7)

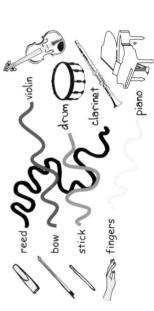

reed

bow

stick

fingers

violin

drum

clarinet

piano

Eleanor's lost letters (page 4)

triangle
claves
xylophone
cymbal
snare drum
tambourine

William's wordsearch (page 13)

A	C	R	O	B	O	C	M	N		
O	L	O	C	C	I	P	O	R		
S	A	X	O	P	H	O	N	E		
I	R	A	L	C	S	B	I	T		
T	I	S	F	S	P	A	H	U		
A	N	J	A	O	A	S	X	L		
L	E	B	L	L	B	O	S	O		
F	T	E	C	I	P	O	X	R		

Which instrument is this?
SAXOPHONE

Oliver's odd-one-out (page 14)

Box	Odd-one-out	Correct box
WOODWIND	tuba	BRASS
STRINGS	flute	WOODWIND
BRASS	triangle	PERCUSSION
PERCUSSION	viola	STRINGS

Thomas's tractor (page 15)

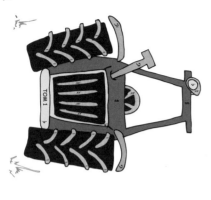

Bethany's brass (page 16)

How many brass instruments are there? **3**
(trumpet, tuba, horn)

How many instruments with strings are there? **5**
(cello, violin, banjo, piano, harp)

Grace's guessing game (page 20)

1. piano
2. cello
3. triangle
4. harp
5. xylophone

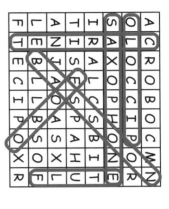

Tyler's train (page 17)

Notes | | | Rests | |
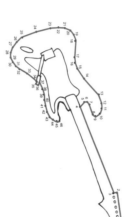

Megan's magic spells (page 21)

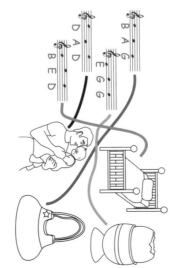

Ella's electric guitar? (page 18)

What's missing from Ella's instrument?
Strings

Dylan's dinosaurs (page 19)

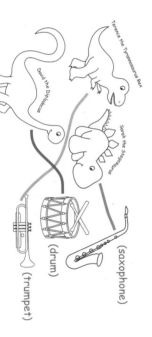

Terence the Tyrannosaurus Rex
David the Diplodocus
Sarah the Stegosaurus
(trumpet)
(drum)
(saxophone)

Callum's crossword (page 22)

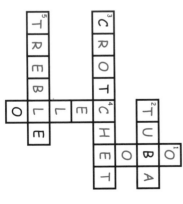